SPACE

To Lins, thanks for our very own
magical adventure! xxx
S.S.

For Jasper, CAR! DINOSAUR! FOOTBALL!
And Andy, who is the best cheerleader I could ask for.
C.C.

By Suzanne Smith • Illustrated by Charlotte Cooke

EGMONT
We bring stories to life

First published in Great Britain 2017 by Egmont UK Limited
This edition published 2018 by Dean,
an imprint of Egmont UK Limited,
The Yellow Building, 1 Nicholas Road, London, W11 4AN
www.egmont.co.uk

Text copyright © Suzanne Smith 2017
Illustrations copyright © Charlotte Cooke 2017
The moral rights of the author and illustrator have been asserted.

ISBN 978 0 6035 7588 4

70189/001

Printed in Malaysia

A CIP catalogue record for this title is available from the British Library.

The Littlest Dreamer
A BEDTIME ADVENTURE

EGMONT

Little one, little one, eyes closed up tight,
What do you **dream** as you sleep through the night?

What will you **see**? What will you **play**?
Will you tell me your dreams when the night becomes day?

Little one, little one, looking at you,
I wonder if all of your dreams will come true.

Do you wish you
could **DRIVE**
in a hurtling chase,

Straight to the finish,
coming first in the race?

FINISH

Would you **ZOOM** around bends in your **FAST RACING CAR**, **WINNING** huge trophies like a world superstar?

Do you wonder, if you were a great **football champ**,

Would your fans in the stands all cheer you and stamp?

As you **run** on the pitch, would you **aim** and then **shoot**...

Scoring a goal with your shiny gold boot?

Do you wish you could **SWIM** to the sandy seabed
And **PLAY SHARK GAMES** for hours with a fun **HAMMERHEAD**?

Would you **DIVE** round the wreck of an old submarine
Through deep ocean waters of brilliant green?

Do you wonder, if **pirates** were hatching a plot,
Could you help them find treasure where **X** marks the spot?
Would you **sail on their ship** to reach faraway lands,
Discovering **gold** buried deep in the sands?

Do you wish you were
a **zookeeper**
at a big zoo,

Where you'd help
feed the **tiger**,

giraffe
or **gnu**?

Would you polish the teeth of the old **crocodile**,

Or tell jokes to the **sloth** just to get him to smile?

Do you wonder, if you were a **knight** on a quest,

Could you find a fierce **dragon** with fire in his chest?

Would you **gallop** along, look him in the eye

And then **save** your pet with your sword held up high?

Do you wonder, if you had a pet **dinosaur**,
Would he be quiet, or would he just **ROAR**?
If you took him to school on "Bring Pets Along" day,
What do you think your class teacher would say?

Do you wish you could be a great **HERO** and **FLY**
In your cape and your mask, past the clouds, through the sky?

Would you put out the flames of hot, roaring fires
And **SAVE THE WHOLE WORLD** with your great superpowers?

Do you wish you could **zooM** in a rocket to **Mars**,

Soaring past planets

and **shooting** past stars?

Would you **fly upside down** through the whole Milky Way
And have fun with an **alien** who asks you to play?

Do your wishes and wonders help you to **sail**
Back home to your bed on a bright stardust trail?

Are you crossing the rooftops over the town
With starlight and moonlight helping you down?

Little one, little one, eyes closed up tight,
What do you **dream** as you sleep through the night?
What will you **see**? What will you **play**?
Will you tell me your dreams when the night becomes day?

Little one, little one, looking at you,

I wonder if all of your dreams will come true.

SPACE